the Good Neighbors

BY

HOLLY BLACK
& TED NAIFEH

book one
KIN

New York   Toronto   London   Auckland   Sydney   Mexico City   New Delhi   Hong Kong   Buenos Aires

WEST CITY, THURSDAY EVENING.

MY NAME IS RUE, LIKE *KANGAROO* OR LIKE "YOU'LL *RUE* THE DAY WE MET, MWA-HA-HA!"

I DON'T SWEAT STUFF. WORRYING JUST GIVES YOU WRINKLE LINES OR STRESS HIVES OR AN ACID STOMACH YOU CAN'T SOOTHE WITH A WHOLE BOX OF TUMS.

4

5

WHATEVER. OUR EYES PLAY TRICKS ON US.

I HEARD THEM ARGUING THE NIGHT SHE DISAPPEARED.

14

YOU SURE YOU'RE OKAY?

I'M *FINE.*

COULDN'T HAVE SAID IT BETTER. YOU'RE SO FINE YOU BLOW MY MIND.

JUSTIN, LUCY, DALE, AND I KIND OF HAVE THIS WEEKEND TRADITION.

WE GET COFFEE.

WE PICK AN ABANDONED BUILDING. ONE WITH SOME HISTORY.

WE BREAK IN.

WE TAKE PICTURES.

AFTER I EXPLAINED HOW LONG MY MOM HAD BEEN GONE, YOU COULD TELL WHAT THEY WERE THINKING.

I CAME AS SOON AS I HEARD.

THE ARRESTING OFFICER SAYS THERE'S REALLY NOTHING WE CAN DO UNTIL THE MORNING.

WHAT DID DAD DO?

23

25

WHY DIDN'T DAD LOOK FOR HER?

WHERE COULD MOM HAVE GONE?

WHAT DID SHE LEAVE BEHIND?

BIRTH CERTIFICATES FOR ME AND MY FATHER, BUT NONE FOR MY MOTHER. NO SOCIAL SECURITY CARD.

WEDDING, BUT NO MARRIAGE LICENSE. NO PICTURES OF MOM AS A KID. SHE LOOKS LIKE SHE'S NEVER AGED.

STRANGE.

27

FRIDAY MORNING.

TODAY, AT SCHOOL, EVERYTHING IS DIFFERENT. THE COLORS SEEM BRIGHTER.

AND, OF COURSE, I'M CRAZY. THAT'S DIFFERENT, TOO.

SARASA WAS AN ENGLISH MAJOR, THE REPORTER SAID.

ACCORDING TO HER BROTHER, SHE STAYED BEHIND TO SPEAK WITH A PROFESSOR.

HER ROOMMATE REPORTED HER MISSING THREE DAYS LATER.

A FRESHMAN FOUND HER BODY.

THEY'RE WAITING FOR US AT THE COURT HOUSE.

WHO?

YOUR MOTHER'S FAMILY.

MY MOTHER'S FAMILY? I DIDN'T KNOW MY MOTHER HAD ... FAMILY. WHERE'S DAD?

BEING ARRAIGNED. HE'S FINE.

YOUR MOTHER'S FATHER'S HERE. HE SAYS HE WANTS YOU TO COME AND LIVE WITH HIM. THAT WOULD BE A VERY BAD IDEA, RUE.

THE BOY FROM THE COFFEEHOUSE.

WHAT ARE *YOU* DOING HERE?

I DON'T KNOW WHAT YOU MEAN.

RUE, THIS IS YOUR GRANDFATHER.

AUBREY. AND MY ASSISTANT, TAM.

44

THE LIBRARY WAS A GREAT COMFORT TO ME WHEN I WAS LITTLE.

THE THING ABOUT A MOM LIKE MINE IS THAT SHE NEVER REALLY UNDERSTOOD HOW TO GIVE ADVICE.

MOM...?

THE KIDS AT SCHOOL LAUGHED WHEN I SAID THAT TREES HAVE THEIR OWN LANGUAGE. AND THE SCIENCE TEACHER SAID –

OH, IT'S SO NICE THAT YOU MADE THEM LAUGH!

IF YOU'RE VERY QUIET, YOU CAN HEAR THE WILLOWS GOSSIPING RIGHT NOW, THE WICKED THINGS. HEAR THEM?

BOOKS GAVE BETTER ADVICE. MOSTLY.

I COULD REALLY USE SOME ADVICE RIGHT ABOUT NOW.

I WANTED TO SEE FOR MYSELF.

A student of Benton College was found dead this morning, after being missing for more than three days. Sarasa Narayan, 19, was last seen by classmates in her Intro to Folklore class in Morton Hall.

Professor Thaddeus Silver has been charged with her murder. Silver is also being questioned in connection with the disappearance of his wife, Nia, 37.

INSTANT MESSAGE

DEVILDALE: r u there?
DEVILDALE: r u there?
DEVILDALE: r u there?

INTERESTS
swimming, flying, travel.

INSTANT MESSAGE

DEVILDALE: r u there?
DEVILDALE: r u there?
DEVILDALE: r u there?
DEVILDALE: r u there?
DEVILDALE: r u there?
DEVILDALE: r u there?

TIPPERARY, IRELAND, 1895.

SHE'S GROWN TWO INCHES TALLER OVERNIGHT. AND SHE'S...SHE'S TOO SURE OF HERSELF. NOT LIKE OUR BRIDGET.

SHE'S SICKLY, MICHAEL. IT'S THE FEVER.

BRIDGET CLEARY WAS FOND OF TAKING LONG WALKS IN THE COUNTRY. HER HUSBAND, MICHAEL, BELIEVED THAT ON ONE OF HER WALKS SHE'D BEEN REPLACED WITH A FAERIE CHANGELING.

WHAT'S WRONG WITH YOU? HAVE YOU ALL GONE MAD?

DRINK THIS, WITCH.

ARE YOU BRIDGET BOLAND, WIFE OF MICHAEL CLEARY, IN THE NAME OF GOD?

YES...YES. YOU KNOW I AM.

47

BRIDGET'S GOING TO RIDE HERE ON A GREY HORSE, BOUND WITH FAERY ROPES AND I NEED TO BE SURE TO CUT HER DOWN. WE'LL ONLY HAVE ONE CHANCE.

THAT'S NOT BRIDGET. DON'T BE FOOLED.

WHAT HAVE YOU DONE?

WHAT PEOPLE WERE MOST SHOCKED BY WAS THAT ANYONE IN 1894 COULD STILL BELIEVE IN FAERIES.

HERE ARE SOME HYPOTHESES I WANT TO TEST:

(A) MY FATHER HAD AN AFFAIR WITH HIS STUDENT AND MY CRAZY MOTHER FOUND OUT AND KILLED THE GIRL IN A JEALOUS RAGE.

(B) MY FATHER HAD AN AFFAIR WITH HIS STUDENT AND MY MOTHER FOUND OUT; DAD KILLED MOM AND THEN THE GIRL.

(C) MY MOTHER WAS STOLEN BY FAERIES THREE WEEKS AGO; THE DEAD GIRL HAS NOTHING TO DO WITH IT.

(D) MY FATHER THOUGHT MY MOTHER WAS A FAERY CHANGELING AND KILLED HER THINKING THAT WOULD BRING MY REAL MOTHER BACK, BUT SHE WASN'T AND NOW SHE'S DEAD; THE DEAD GIRL STILL HAS NOTHING TO DO WITH IT.

EVERYONE SAYS THE SAME THINGS ABOUT KILLERS: "HE WAS SO NICE. HE MOWED THAT OLD LADY'S LAWN FOR NOTHING, TOOK AN OLD 80 POUND BAG OF QUICKLIME OFF MY HANDS."

YOU DON'T THINK YOUR DAD DID IT, DO YOU?

THIS IS WHERE THE GIRL WAS LAST. WE'RE USED TO CREEPING AROUND PLACES. MAYBE WE CAN FIND SOMETHING.

THERE'S NOT GOING TO BE ANYTHING THE POLICE HAVEN'T ALREADY GOT.

COME ON. IF IT WAS MY DAD, I'D WANT TO DO SOMETHING, TOO. CUT SOME SLACK.

HAVE YOU NOTICED THE VINES AROUND HERE ARE GOING CRAZY? I HEARD SOMETHING ON THE NEWS. POISON IVY IS BIGGER AND DEADLIER BECAUSE OF GLOBAL WARMING AND--

SHHHH!

DO YOU THINK THIS COULD BE A CLUE?

WAIT! WHAT ARE YOU?

AAAAUGH!

THEN THE SHADOW IS GONE AND I'M FALLING.

I REACH OUT FOR THE VINES AND IT'S WEIRD BECAUSE THE VINES REACH FOR ME BACK.

THEY DO WHAT I WANT.

WHAT JUST HAPPENED?

IT'S LIKE RAPPELLING OFF A ROOFTOP.

WITHOUT THE ROPE.

AMAZING.

I'M VERY SORRY TO STARTLE YOU.

I DON'T TRUST YOU. OR AUBREY. YOU CAN TELL HIM SO.

GOOD.

BUT I'M NOT HERE FOR AUBREY.

STALKING ME, TAM?

I'M CURSED. SOMETIMES I SAY TRUE THINGS, THINGS MY CURSE KNOWS BUT I DON'T. USUALLY WHEN I'M ASKED A QUESTION.

SOMETIMES I DON'T EVEN REMEMBER WHAT I SAID.

FOR ONCE, I'M NOT THE ONLY ONE PRETENDING EVERYTHING'S OKAY.

HE-E-EY GIRL, YOU CUT ME LIKE A RA-A-A-ZOR. YOU GU-UT ME, CU-UT ME, GU-UT ME, CU-UT ME.

NOW I KNOW THE LOOK.

HE'S AFRAID.

OF ME.

THANKS FOR COMING. GOOD NIGHT, EVERYONE!

YOU WERE REALLY WONDERFUL.

MY SISTERS AND I LIKE TO SING.

WOULD YOU LIKE TO HEAR US?

SOME CHOICE.

SO... I DON'T SUPPOSE I CAN LEAVE?

NO.

PLEEEEEASE?

I'M BOUND TO AUBREY.

HIS WILL COMMANDS ME.

DAD'S LAWYERS SAY THAT MOM TURNING UP MADE THE PROSECUTION'S LAWYERS LOOK STUPID.

IT WAS A PUBLIC RELATIONS NIGHTMARE. SINCE DAD'S ALIBI FOR SARASA'S MURDER SEEMED TO HOLD UP AND MY MOTHER OBVIOUSLY HADN'T BEEN KILLED, THEY HAD TO LET HIM GO. THE MEDIA LOVED IT.

POOF! CHARGES DROPPED.

LIKE IT NEVER HAPPENED.

BUT I STILL WONDER ABOUT SARASA.

NAVEEN

KNOCK!
KNOCK!

IT'S EASIER TO CREEP
AROUND NOW THAT I CAN
MAKE MYSELF INVISIBLE.

NOT EXACTLY LIKE BREAKING
INTO AN ABANDONED BUILDING.

BUT NOT AS DIFFERENT
AS YOU'D FIGURE.

TOO MANY FOR IT TO BE FROM A LEAKY COMFORTER.

NOT THE KIND USED IN PILLOWS. THE LONG ONES.

ALL OF THEM, WHITE AS SNOW.

YOU'RE NAVEEN, AREN'T YOU? SARASA'S BROTHER.

I FIND HIM THE FIRST PLACE I LOOK.

YOU'RE NOT HUMAN.

NEITHER ARE YOU.

WES HAS YOUR SWAN SKIN, DOESN'T HE? THAT'S WHY YOU COULDN'T STOP HIM FROM KILLING HER, ISN'T IT?

IT'S NOT YOUR FAULT.

IF THAT WAS ALL I DID, IT WOULD BE ENOUGH.

BUT I HAVE DONE MUCH MORE.

SINCE WE WERE CHILDREN, WE'VE TRAVELED TOGETHER. NO HOME. NO NEED FOR ONE.

ALL WE NEEDED WAS FREEDOM.

WE THOUGHT IT WOULD BE INTERESTING TO GO TO SCHOOL FOR A TIME.

THERE WERE SO MANY THINGS TO LEARN.

MY SISTER WAS A FLIRT.

SOON SHE HAD – WHAT DO YOU SAY? – BOYS EATING OUT OF HER HANDS.

WES WAS MERELY ONE OF THEM.

THE ONLY DIFFERENCE WAS THAT HE DISCOVERED US.

HIS EYES NEVER LEFT HER.

HE MUST HAVE FOLLOWED US AND GUESSED THE REST.

SHE HAD TO PLAY THE PART OF HIS LOVING SLAVE.

AND I HAD TO LET HER.

WHAT YOU DON'T UNDERSTAND IS HOW MUCH OUR FREEDOM MATTERED.

WE'D RATHER DIE THAN BE CAPTIVES.

I WENT TO LOCAL FAERIES. BEFORE. THEY WOULDN'T HELP US GET THE SWAN SKINS BACK.

THEY WOULDN'T DO ANYTHING BUT USE SARASA'S DEATH TO CAUSE TROUBLE FOR SOME MORTAL.

WES TOLD US WE COULDN'T KILL OURSELVES. AS LONG AS HE HAS MY CAPE, I MUST OBEY HIM.

BUT YOU COULD. FOR SARASA. AVENGE HER. PLEASE.

NO.

MAYBE I SHOULD FEEL BAD FOR HIM.

I FEEL NOTHING.

YOU CAN ALWAYS COUNT ON YOUR FAMILY TO LOVE YOU.

AND TO BETRAY YOU.

AND THEN TO FEEL GUILTY ABOUT IT.

AMANDA'S BEEN REALLY GOOD TO ME AND DAD.

TOO GOOD. GUILTY GOOD.

DAD'S DUMPY FRIEND, WHO SEEMS VERY DISTRACTED THESE DAYS.

WHAT DID YOU AND MY DAD DO? WHAT DID YOU DO TO MY MOM?

YOU DARE COURT MY DAUGHTER WITHOUT MY PERMISSION?

I'M SORRY. I DIDN'T KNOW—

THAT SHE WAS MY DAUGHTER? THAT SHE WASN'T JUST SOME MAID YOU COULD STEAL THE SKIN OF AND CARRY OFF?

I WOULD NEVER DO ANYTHING TO HURT NIA. I LOVE HER.

MORTALS ARE INCONSTANT LOVERS.

MY PERMISSION WAS GIVEN, FATHER. YOURS DOES NOT SUPERCEDE MINE.

111

DALE WOULDN'T COME.

MAYBE HE'S NOT THE GUY I THOUGHT HE WAS.

MAYBE I'M NOT THE GIRL HE THOUGHT I WAS EITHER.

WHAT KIND OF GIRL WOULD DIG UP HER MOM, AFTER ALL?

SHE'S NOT GOING TO RISE UP HUNGERING FOR BRAINS, RIGHT?

JUST DIG.

I JUST HAD TO SEE IF IT WAS REALLY HER IN THERE.

IF THERE'S ANYTHING IN THERE AT ALL.

MY EYES ARE WIDE OPEN NOW.

I SEE EVERYTHING.

end of book one

ABOUT THE AUTHOR

Holly Black is the author of contemporary fantasy novels for teens and children. Born in New Jersey, Holly grew up in a decrepit Victorian house piled with books and oddments. She never quite recovered.

Her first book, *Tithe: A Modern Faerie Tale*, was called "dark, edgy, beautifully written and compulsively readable" by *Booklist*, received starred reviews from *Publisher's Weekly* and *Kirkus*, and was included in the American Library Association's Best Books for Young Adults. Holly has since written two other books in the same universe, *Valiant*, a recipient of the Andre Norton Award for Excellence in Young Adult Literature, and *Ironside*.

Holly collaborated with her long-time friend, Caldecott Honor–winning artist Tony DiTerlizzi, to create the best-selling Spiderwick Chronicles. The serial has been called "vintage Victorian fantasy" by the *New York Post*, and *Time Magazine* reported that "the books wallow in their dusty Olde Worlde charm." The Spiderwick Chronicles were adapted into a film in 2008.

She is currently working on a curse magic caper novel called *The White Cat*.

Holly lives in Massachusetts with her husband, Theo, and an ever-expanding collection of books. She spends a lot of her time in cafes, glaring at her laptop and drinking endless cups of coffee.

ABOUT THE ARTIST

Ted Naifeh swooped onto the comics and goth culture scene as the co-creator of *Gloomcookie* with Serena Valentino in 1998. Ted illustrated the first volume of the gothic romance hit before departing to pursue his own projects.

In 2002, he introduced us to the world of Courtney Crumrin, a young loner girl who learns magic from her mysterious and curmudgeonly Uncle Aloysius and uses it to navigate her world of school bullies and bloodthirsty goblins, adolescent peer pressure and deadly coven politics. Courtney's adventures have been published in five volumes: *Courtney Crumrin and the Night Things*, *Courtney Crumrin and the Coven of Mystics*, *Courtney Crumrin in the Twilight Kingdom*, *Courtney Crumrin and the Fire-Thief's Tale*, and *Courtney Crumrin and the Prince of Nowhere*.

Ted's next creation was *Polly and the Pirates*, also published through Oni Press, a swashbuckling tale of proper, rule-abiding young Polly Pringle, who is spirited away from her comfortable boarding school existence by pirates who insist that she is their rightful queen and captain. *Polly and the Pirates* was nominated for a Harvey Award.

Ted has also illustrated six volumes featuring video game character Death Jr. for Image Comics, and is the co-creator of *How Loathsome*, strictly for the 18-and-up crowd.

Ted lives in San Francisco, which influenced his aesthetic from a young age with its magnificently spooky Victorian houses, romantic foggy nights, and significant population of Night Things and other fantastic beings.

ACKNOWLEDGMENTS

A lot of people had a hand in pushing me to try writing a graphic novel and helping me along the way. Thanks to Jon Shestack and Ellen Goldsmith-Vein in particular, for asking me about another faery story and liking the one that I told them. Thanks to Steve Burkow for his calm counsel. I am indebted to my literary agent, Barry Goldblatt, and to my editor, the ever-encouraging and amazing David Levithan. And to Ted Naifeh, who brought these characters to life.

I am grateful to Cecil Castellucci, Kelly Link, Justine Larbalestier, Steve Berman, and Cassandra Clare for pushing me to write better and more cleverly. Thanks to Theo for letting me know when things made sense. And thanks to all of you for putting up with my whingeing.

I was greatly inspired by two books, *The Cooper's Wife Is Missing* by Joan Hoff and Marian Yeates and *The Burning of Bridget Cleary* by Angela Bourke. This book was written with the program Scrivener.

– **Holly Black**

I'd like to thank my girlfriend, Kelly, for pestering Cassie Clare into friendship, and Cassie for suggesting me to Holly. Thanks to both Cassie and Holly for not freaking out at us weird San Francisco kids. I'd also like to thank Phil Falco for the gentle, cheerful nudging, and for being a friendly voice getting me out of bed before the day was completely wasted. Sorry it ran so late.

– **Ted Naifeh**